Happy Reading!

♡ Katie Lee

This book is dedicated to its reader.
It is meant to heal its reader and lift the
spell that was put on humanity so long ago.

To my sisters, you know who you are.
To my loves, Brian, Ella, Ty & Averie.

- K.L.

To buy more books or receive a signed copy, visit the author's website at:
www.gallerybykatielee.com

Graphic Design: Brittany Lee
Photo Credit: Russell Hons Photography
Editors: Ashley McEnroe & Barb Bergner

Published by Katie Lee
PO Box 13458, Grand Forks, ND 58208

ISBN 978-1-7337816-0-2

Library of Congress Cataloging-in-Publication Data

Publisher's Cataloging-In-Publication Data
(Prepared by The Donohue Group, Inc.)

Names: Lee, Katie, 1984- author, illustrator.
Title: No matter your color the Great Spirit will find you / written & illustrated by Katie Lee.
Description: Grand Forks, ND : Katie Lee, 2019. | Interest age level: 0 and up. | Summary: "A young girl discovers an ancient Native American medicine wheel on her parents' ranch. Through her discovery, she is taken on a spiritual journey and taught an important lesson in life. She finds out that no matter our color or beliefs we are all the same on the inside."–Provided by publisher.
Identifiers: ISBN 9781733781602 | ISBN 9781733781619 (ebook)
Subjects: LCSH: Medicine wheels–Juvenile fiction. | Ranches–Juvenile fiction. | Equality–Juvenile fiction. | Spirituality–Juvnile fiction.| Bullying–Juvenile fiction. | Self-acceptance–Juvenile fiction. CYAC: Ranches–Fiction. | Equality–Fiction. | Spirituality–Fiction. | Bullying–Fiction. | Self-acceptance–Fiction.
Classification: LCC PZ7.1.L44 No 2019 (print) | LCC PZ7.1.L44 (ebook) | DDC [E]–dc23

Library of Congress Control Number – 2019903358

Printed in the United States of America

The artwork was created with oil paints, a palette knife and a brush.

No Matter Your COLOR

the Great Spirit Will Find You

Written & Illustrated by Katie Lee

One night before bed, little Ella wished on seven stars.
They are her seven sisters, neither near nor far.

She wished that all people could see they are ONE
and whispered, "Please lift this spell and the job will be done."

As nature awoke the very next day,
a dream of a spider and his web came into play.

Ella remembered what the wise spider had told her...

"Humanity is like my web all woven together."

That day on Grandpa's ranch looking for cool rocks,

Ella found ancient stones protected by a fox.

She asked why the stones were in the shape of a wheel.
He replied...

"Ancient people put them there as a way to heal."

The rest of the day she thought of what the fox said.

That night she prayed...

and prayed before bed...

If only that stone wheel could heal all mankind
and break down borders we create with our mind.

At once humanity would see we are ONE,
we could put away the rest and see life is fun!

The next morning before the day was to break,
Ella went back to the stones and was surprised by a snake.

The snake told her, "I am a symbol in your life,
coiled and coiled I'm both goodness and strife.

Go to the very edge of the stony wheel,
ask for permission to enter and heal."

Ella did just that and without even a word,
paused for a moment and that's when she heard...

the sound of deep breaths in her right ear
but looking around she found no one near.

That is the moment the Great Spirit spoke...

"Ella, my dear, it's nice you awoke.

The spell that was put on all people long ago,
is starting to lift and we are starting to GLOW.

Soon all people will know they are ONE
and YOU are here to see this gets done."

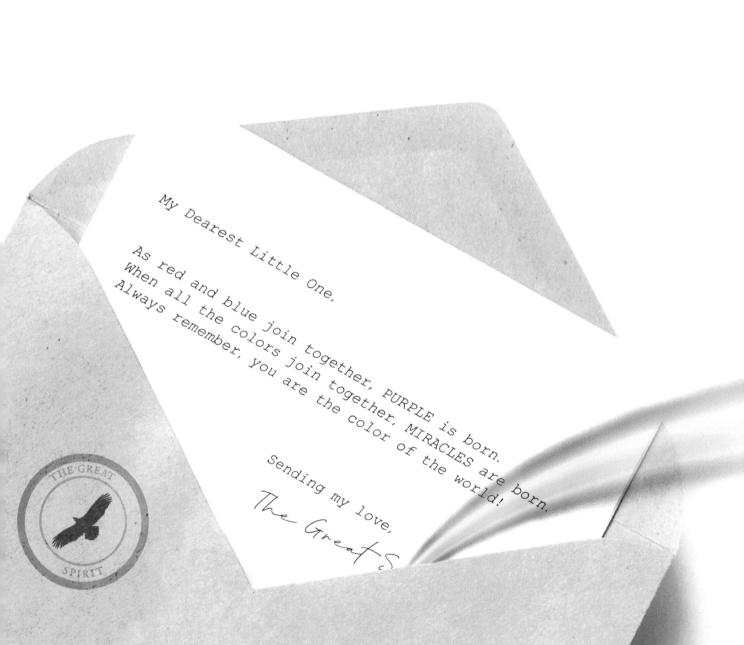

My Dearest Little One,

As red and blue join together, PURPLE is born.
When all the colors join together, MIRACLES are born.
Always remember, you are the color of the world!

Sending my love,
The Great S

THE GREAT
SPIRIT

The Author's True-Life Story

In 2015, I had the idea to paint a real 18-foot-tall teepee that I would display in Big Sky, Montana. I started researching the traditional Native American teepee painting process and learned that knowing what to paint typically comes from a vision or dream. One morning, I decided to do a sunrise meditation. I woke up just before sunrise and went out to an open field about a mile from my parents' ranch house in western North Dakota. The previous year, my dad had found what looked like an old teepee ring near the edge of this field which I thought would make a perfect spot for my meditation. Approaching the circle of stones, I intuitively stopped before entering. Something inside me decided I should ask permission to enter first. So, I reached both hands out to the sky, closed my eyes and quietly, to myself, asked the Spirit to allow me to enter this sacred space. In that moment, while my eyes were closed, I heard what sounded like a bison standing right behind me. I heard the deepest inhale and exhale and again inhale and exhale into my right ear. My heart skipped a beat, my mind raced through every possible scenario of what I was about to witness. I braced myself, opened my eyes and was in complete awe to see the same wide-open field through which I had just walked. There were no animals and no people as far as the eye could see. How could this be?

Later that day I spoke to a very spiritual friend that lives in the area and told her about my experience. Early the very next morning, she told me that a native man came to her in her dream. He presented himself as Iktomi, a name she had never heard of before. He told her the breaths I experienced was the Spirit cleansing me before entering the sacred space. He also told her it was not a teepee ring I walked into but an ancient medicine wheel dating

Photo Credit Hope Ann Photography

back thousands of years. He explained to her that the medicine wheel was used for spiritual and healing ceremonies and to teach humanity about the eternal circle of life. He also spoke of how they were typically built high on a bluff, overlooking water and facing the morning sun, which was exactly how this one was positioned. A few days later I awoke early one morning to the thought that maybe Iktomi had been a real Native American at one time, so I decided to Google his name to see what I could find. I found out that Iktomi was the name of the Great Spider Spirit in Lakota mythology and is best known for being the legend of the dreamcatcher. My spiritual friend decided to contact a Native American acquaintance living on the Standing Rock Reservation and told him of the events that had taken place. He promptly invited us to his home for a sweat lodge ceremony. He explained, after having such an experience, that a sweat should take place. In the early fall of that year, three of my "sisters" and I headed to the Standing Rock Reservation for our first-ever sweat lodge ceremony. To explain in detail the things that happened that day would be nearly impossible but what I will never forget is the wisdom that was shared with me. I had inquired why this experience in the medicine wheel had happened to me, a non-Native American, white girl, from North Dakota. I was told that the Spirit does not see the color of our skin but can only see the color of our soul. It moved me to tears and, in that moment, it seemed so obvious to me that it has always been humans who created these borders around ourselves. I had wrongly assumed the Spirit also saw these same borders. I will be forever changed from this experience and my hope is, through this book, I can help change how people see the world.

-Katie Lee

P.S. Always keep an open mind especially with little ones. You never know what someone else's world looks like. The world a child envisions might be a far greater one than we have created. Shutting them down will only halt our progression toward peace on earth!

Photo Credit Nick Brown